VOCALS

TRINITY
COLLEGE LONDON

THE EXAM
AT A GLANCE

For your Rock & Pop exam you will need to perform a set of **three songs** and one of the **Session skills** assessments, either **Playback** or **Improvising**. You can choose the order in which you play your set-list.

Song 1

Choose a song from this book

OR from www.trinityrock.com

Song 2

Choose a different song from this book

OR from www.trinityrock.com

OR perform a song you have chosen yourself: this could be your own cover version or a song you have written. It should be at the same level as the songs in this book. See the website for detailed requirements.

Song 3: Technical focus

Choose one of the Technical focus songs from this book, which cover three specific technical elements.

Session skills

Choose either **Playback** or **Improvising**.

When you are preparing for your exam please check on **www.trinityrock.com** for the most up-to-date information and requirements as these can change from time to time.

CONTENTS

Trinity College London's Rock & Pop syllabus and supporting publications have been devised and produced in association with Faber Music and Peters Edition London.

Trinity College London
Registered office:
89 Albert Embankment
London SE1 7TP UK
T + 44 (0)20 7820 6100
F + 44 (0)20 7820 6161
E music@trinitycollege.co.uk
www.trinitycollege.co.uk

Registered in the UK. Company no. 02683033
Charity no. 1014792
Patron HRH The Duke of Kent KG

Copyright © 2012 Trinity College London
First published in 2012 by Trinity College London

Cover and book design by Chloë Alexander
Brand development by Andy Ashburner @ Caffeinehit (www.caffeinehit.com)
Photographs courtesy of Rex Features Limited.
Printed in England by Caligraving Ltd

Audio produced, mixed and mastered by Tom Fleming
Vocal arrangements by Oliver Weeks
Backing tracks arranged by Tom Fleming
Vocal Consultant: Heidi Pegler
Musicians
Vocals: Bo Walton, Brendan Reilly & Alison Symons
Keyboards: Oliver Weeks
Guitar: Tom Fleming
Bass: Ben Hillyard
Drums: George Double
Studio Engineer: Joel Davies www.thelimehouse.com

All rights reserved

ISBN: 978-0-85736-259-9

SONGS PRICE TAG

Jessie J
Words and Music by Claude Kelly, Bobby Simmons, Lukasz Gottwald and Jessica Cornish

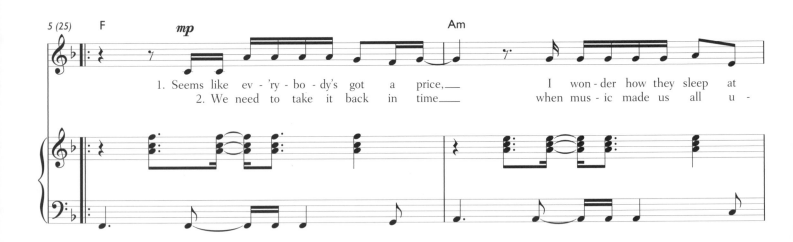

1. Seems like ev-'ry-bo-dy's got a price,___ I won-der how they sleep at
2. We need to take it back in time___ when mus-ic made us all u-

night when the sale comes first and the truth comes sec-ond, just stop for a min-ute and
-nite! And it wasn't low blows and___ vi-deo woes___ am I the on-ly one get-ting...

Alternative higher key available from www.trinityrock.com

SONGS

THE GREATEST LOVE OF ALL

Whitney Houston
Lyrics by Linda Creed • Music by Michael Masser

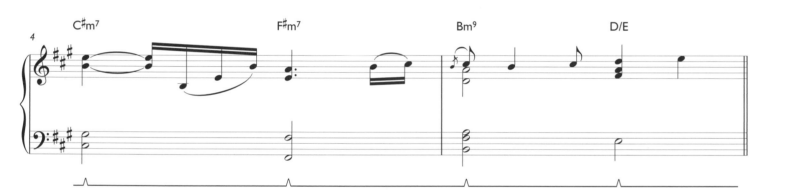

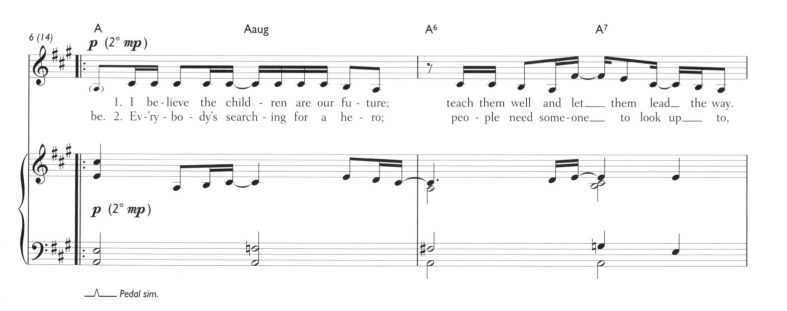

1. I be-lieve the child-ren are our fu-ture; teach them well and let__ them lead__ the way.

be. 2. Ev-'ry-bo-dy's search-ing for a he-ro; peo-ple need some-one__ to look up__ to,

Alternative higher key available from www.trinityrock.com

Show them all the beau-ty they pos-sess in - side.
I ne - ver found a - ny - one who ful-filled my needs.

Give them a
A lone - ly

sense of pride, to make it ea - si - er;___ let the child-ren's
place to be, and so I

laugh - - ter re - mind us how___ we used to

BAND OPTION

SONGS THE RAGGLE TAGGLE GYPSIES

TRACK 5 demo   TRACK 6 backing

Trad.
Words and Music Trad.

♩ = 90 **Fast folk feel** *2 bars count-in*

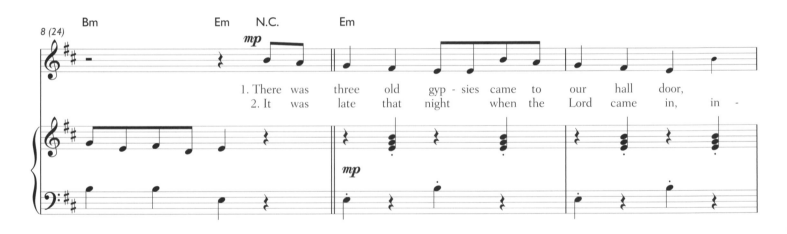

1. There was three old gyp-sies came to our hall door,
2. It was late that night when the our Lord came in, in-

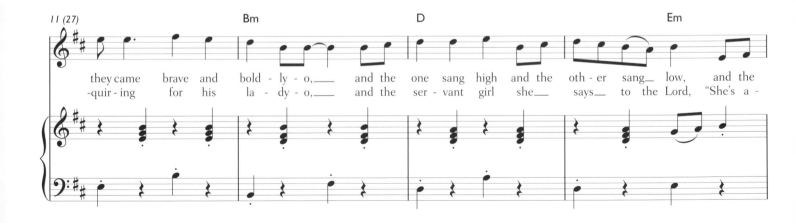

they came brave and bold-ly-o,___ and the one sang high and the oth-er sang___ low, and the
-quir-ing for his la-dy-o,___ and the ser-vant girl she___ says___ to the Lord, "She's a-

www.trinityrock.com

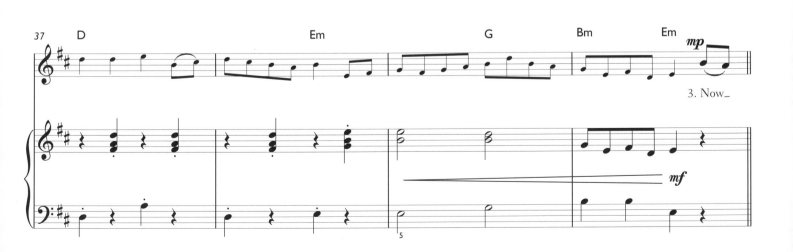

what care I for my house and land? What care I for mon - ey - o?____ I'd

rath - er have a kiss from a yel - low gyp - sy's lips, I'm a - way with the rag - gle tag - gle gyp - sy - o!

SONGS ONE DAY LIKE THIS

Elbow

Words and Music by Guy Garvey, Craig Potter, Mark Potter, Peter Turner and Richard Jupp

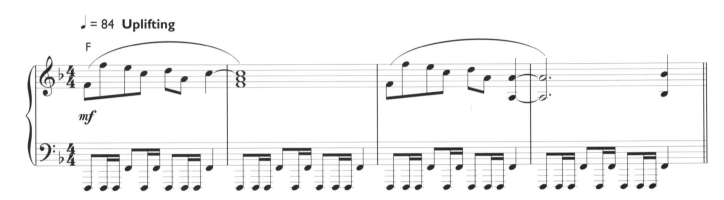

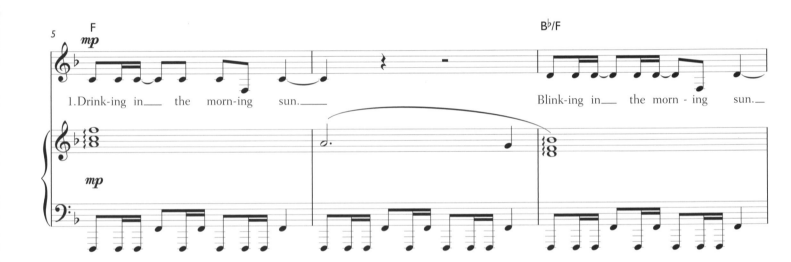

1. Drink-ing in the morn-ing sun. Blink-ing in the morn-ing sun.

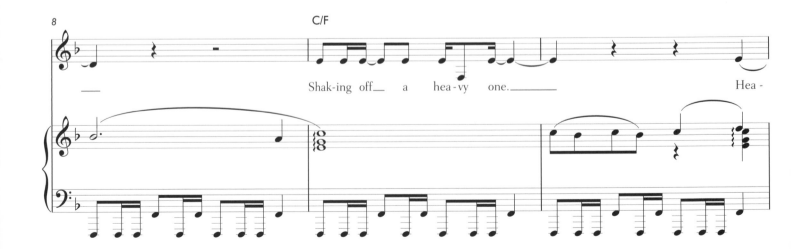

Shak-ing off a hea-vy one. Hea-

Alternative lower key available from www.trinityrock.com

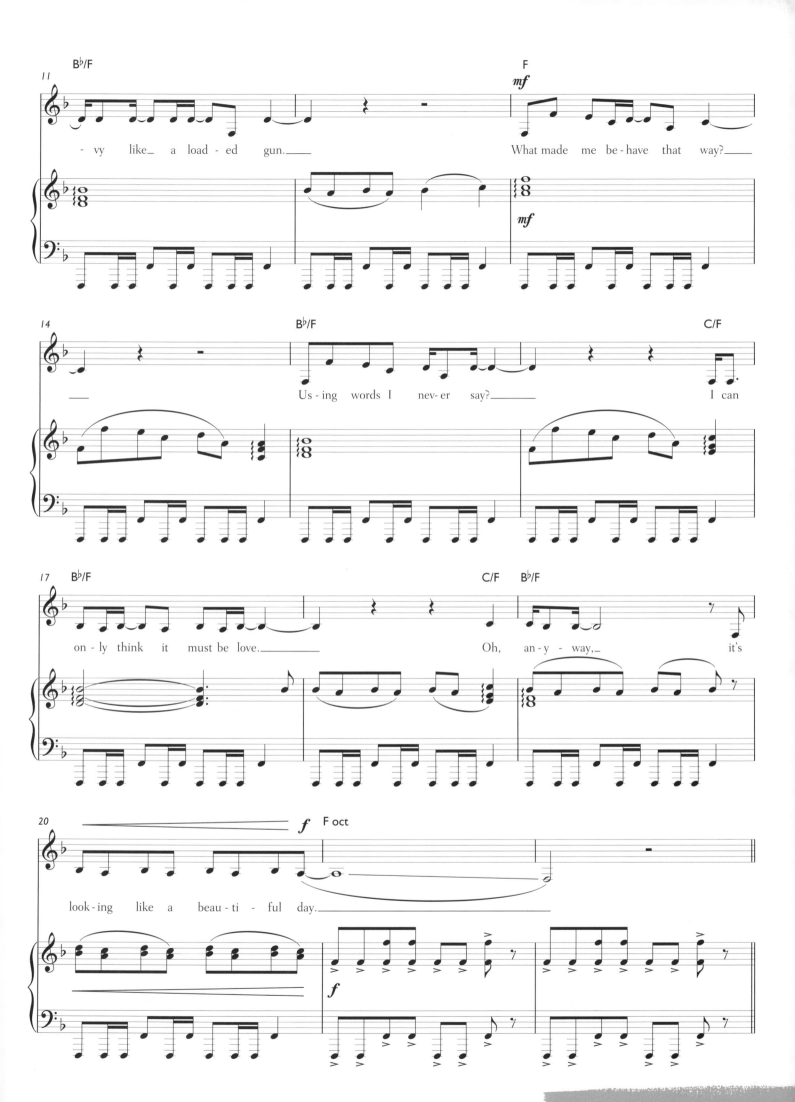

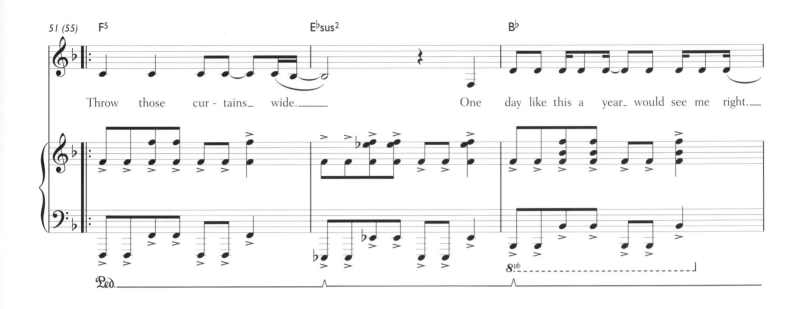

Throw those cur - tains__ wide._____ One day like this a year__ would see me right.__

__ Throw those cur - tains__ wide._____ One

day like this a year___ would see me right.___

EVERYBODY HURTS

In your exam, you will be assessed on the following technical elements:

1 Rhythmic control

Most phrases in 'Everybody Hurts' start on an off-beat ♪ note. Aim to make confident and precise entries – it will help if you listen to the ♪ notes in the accompaniment. Be aware that the time signature is $\frac{12}{8}$, so the beat is subdivided into three ♪ notes.

2 Phrasing

This song is made up of a series of short phrases. These should not sound disjointed – instead, think of them in groups, forming longer musical lines. Keep a sense of narrative, telling the story and building from one phrase to the next.

3 Dynamic range

'Everybody Hurts' uses a wide dynamic range. The verses are marked *mp* but the climax of the song – at the words 'Don't throw your hand' – is marked *f*. Then, at bar 46, the dynamic level suddenly drops back to *mp*, and then to *pp* at the end. Make sure that these differences can be heard.

TECHNICAL FOCUS SONGS

TRACK 9 demo   TRACK 10 backing

EVERYBODY HURTS

R.E.M.
Words and Music by William Berry, Michael Stipe, Peter Buck and Michael Mills

1. When the day is long____
2. When your day is night a -

- lone,
and the night,____ the night is yours____ a - lone,
if you feel like let - ting go,____

VOCALS GRADE 5

Alternative higher key available from www.trinityrock.com

YOUR PAGE NOTES

MOONDANCE

In your exam, you will be assessed on the following technical elements:

1 Diction

Diction refers to clarity of pronunciation. The words in the verses of 'Moondance' are very descriptive and need to be clear. Aim for bright vowels and crisp consonants. Don't forget about the endings of words – for example, make sure that you articulate the 'sh' sound on 'hush' (bar 24) and 'blush' (bar 28). Try not to overdo it though – you should make the words comprehensible but not artificial.

2 Polyrhythms

A polyrhythm is when two or more rhythms with different pulses are heard together – two against three, for example. 'Moondance' uses polyrhythms in bars 18 and 19, where the accompaniment has four ♩ beats in a bar while the vocal line has two consecutive triplets – six ♩ notes in a bar. Make sure that the triplet notes flow evenly.

3 Breathing

Work out where you are going to breathe in 'Moondance'. The song has many four-bar phrases, but several phrases are shorter and some are much longer. Experiment with singing more than one phrase in a single breath. In verse 2, for example, you could avoid taking a breath in bar 56 and carry on through from 'you just tremble inside' to 'and I know how much you want me that'.

Take particular care with the breathing on the final page, where there is a slower tempo and a long sustained note on the word 'love'. Make sure you don't breathe mid-phrase.

MOONDANCE

TRACK 11 demo
TRACK 12 backing

Van Morrison
Words and Music by Van Morrison

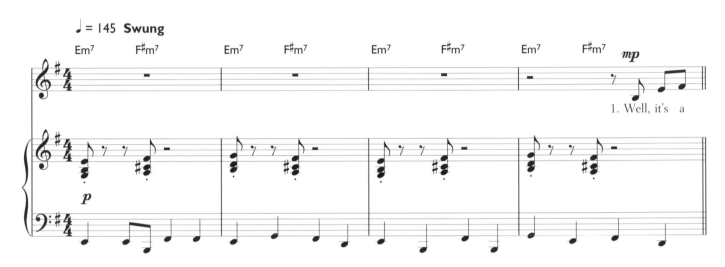

♩ = 145 **Swung**

1. Well, it's a

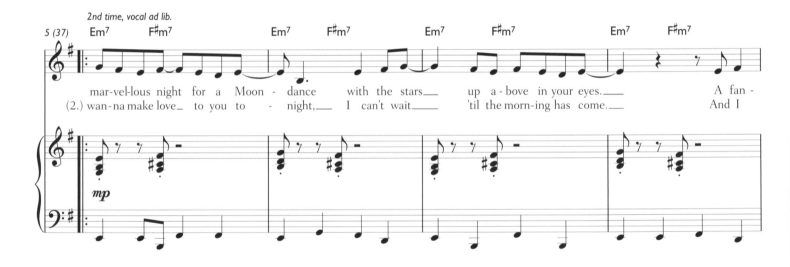

2nd time, vocal ad lib.

mar-vel-lous night for a Moon - dance with the stars__ up a - bove in your eyes.__ A fan -
(2.) wan-na make love__ to you to - night,__ I can't wait__ 'til the morn-ing has come.__ And I

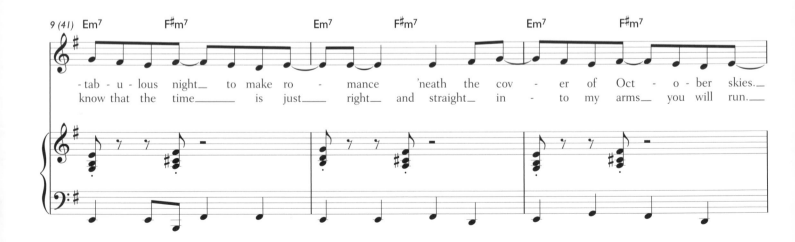

-tab-u - lous night__ to make ro - mance 'neath the cov - er of Oct - o - ber skies.__
know that the time__ is just__ right__ and straight__ in - to my arms__ you will run.

Alternative higher key available from www.trinityrock.com

PRICE TAG

Jessie J

Jessie J began her career in showbiz at the age of 11 with a role in Andrew Lloyd Webber's West End production of *Whistle Down the Wind*. She went on to study at The BRIT School – the London performing arts school famous for producing international stars such as Amy Winehouse and Adele.

Jessie J first rose to fame writing songs for other people, including Chris Brown and Miley Cyrus. 'Price Tag' comes from her debut album *Who You Are* (2011).

This song is driven by the natural rhythm of the words so it is worth speaking the text several times before you sing it in order to get a feel for the rhythm. In 'Price Tag', the more important words are usually given longer note values.

You have to communicate a lot of text in this song – much of it sung to ♪ and ♪ notes. Articulate the consonants clearly – they will give the song energy and enable the listener to understand you more easily. When you arrive on longer notes (for example, the words 'world' at bar 19 and 'price' at bar 20) take the opportunity to really sing out.

The chorus should be bouncy and rhythmical. This is a carefree song: try to convey this through your singing.

Remember that if this key doesn't suit your voice there is an alternative version available from www.trinityrock.com in a higher key.

'We need to take it back in time'

THE GREATEST LOVE OF ALL

Whitney Houston

Whitney Houston (1963 – 2012) was one of the biggest pop stars of all time. She came from a musical family – her mother Cissy Houston was a soul and gospel singer and her cousin is the singer Dionne Warwick. She began singing with a gospel group at the age of 11 and, as a teenager, worked as a backing vocalist. She is most famous for her passionate ballads and virtuosic singing, incorporating flashy melodic embellishments.

In the 1980s Whitney Houston became the first ever artist to have seven consecutive hit singles. 'The Greatest Love Of All' is one of her most successful international hit singles. In 1986 she named her first headlining world tour after the song – The Greatest Love Tour.

PERFORMANCE HINTS & TIPS

This is a slow passionate ballad. It starts *p*, increasing to *mp* for verse 2, then *mf* at bar 20 and *f* at bar 33. Make sure that you hold something in reserve before bar 33 so that you can sing loud without shouting.

Take care at bar 26 – this single bar of $\frac{2}{4}$ is marked *poco rall.* (= *poco rallentando*), which means you should gradually slow down a little, returning to the original speed (*a tempo*) in bar 27.

Plan where to breathe. Make sure you don't breathe mid-phrase – try to follow the punctuation of the words. Hold the final note for its full value, using plenty of support so that it does not go out of tune.

Remember that if this key doesn't suit your voice there is an alternative version available from www.trinityrock.com in a higher key.

'Ev'rybody's searching for a hero'

THE RAGGLE TAGGLE GYPSIES

Trad.

'The Raggle Taggle Gypsies' probably comes from Scotland – the first printed version dates from the early 18th century. The song came to be associated with the legendary love story of the gypsy Johnny Faa and Lady Jean Hamilton. In 1609, gypsies were expelled from Scotland and their love affair ended. Lady Jean married an earl but, years later, Johnny Faa returned and persuaded her to elope. The couple were caught; Johnny Faa and seven other gypsies were hanged and Lady Jean was imprisoned in a tower for the rest of her life.

There are many covers of this song, notably by The Waterboys, The Chieftains and Alison Moyet.

'The Raggle Taggle Gypsies' has a folk two-in-a-bar feel. The melody is fairly simple and all the verses are quite similar – the challenge is to tell the story at a fast tempo. There are several characters – the servant girl, the lord, the gypsy and the lady – consider giving each character its own vocal quality and characterisation.

Use the printed dynamics to make the song dramatic. Much of the song is marked **_mp_**, getting louder for the last line of each verse. The loudest part of the song is the end of the final verse.

The final verse should be louder – **_mf_**, rising to **_f_** at the end of the verse. Much of this verse is unaccompanied – you will need a good sense of timing and pitch to keep it rhythmically secure and in tune.

This song is also in the bass, guitar, keyboards and drums books, so you can get together and perform it in a band.

'How *could* you *leave* your *only* wedded *Lord?*'

ONE DAY LIKE THIS

Elbow

The members of Elbow met in the early 1990s whilst studying at college in Manchester. They describe their music as 'prog without the solos' and cite a number of musical influences – including Genesis and Radiohead. They are an atmospheric band with a wide dynamic and emotional range.

'One Day Like This' is from Elbow's album *The Seldom Seen Kid*, recorded in Manchester in 2008. It was produced and mixed by their keyboard player Craig Potter.

Practise singing some of the larger intervals in 'One Day Like This' before you learn to sing the whole song. There is a fifth in bar 5, a sixth in bar 7, a seventh in bar 9 and an octave in bar 13. Sing these intervals cleanly – be sure you know which notes you are jumping from and to.

You will need to take a big breath before the phrases starting at the end of bars 19 and 37. This will enable you to sing the whole phrase strongly in one breath – sustaining the final note for its full value. Make sure that you support all the long notes so that they stay in tune.

There is a vocal slide between the notes in bars 21 and 22. Don't start this too soon – sliding on just the last beat of the bar would work well.

Remember that if this key doesn't suit your voice there is an alternative version available from www.trinityrock.com in a lower key.

'It's silly wrong but vivid right'

EVERYBODY HURTS

R.E.M.

R.E.M. is widely regarded as one of the world's most successful rock bands of recent years. Michael Stipe (vocals), Peter Buck (guitar), Michael Mills (bass) and Bill Berry (drums) formed R.E.M. in Georgia, US in 1980, determined not to conform to traditional rock music rules.

'Everybody Hurts' was first released in 1992 on R.E.M.'s eighth album – *Automatic For The People*. It was aimed at teenagers and is a message for people in doubt or despair: at its climax it offers a glimpse of hope. Notable for its direct and devastating lyrics, the song has been used by countless charities and is now a classic of modern rock.

'Everybody Hurts' starts with an interval of a minor seventh – practise this until you can pitch it accurately and securely. The same interval appears in bars 7 and 9 but be ready for bars 13 and 15, where the interval is a fifth.

Wherever the word 'hurts' appears, hold it for its full length. This will give emphasis to the title of the song. Bars 20 and 22 contain quadruplets – indicated by a ⌐—4—⌐ sign. This means that you sing four ♪ in the time of three. Be sure to make all four notes the same length.

From bar 37, the music takes on a slightly rockier feel, until the last five bars return to the style of the opening.

Remember that if this key doesn't suit your voice there is an alternative version available from www.trinityrock.com in a higher key.

'Don't *throw* your *hand*, oh, *no*'

MOONDANCE

Van Morrison

Van Morrison's music is characterised by his soulful, often melancholy voice and improvisatory, free vocal delivery. He has been making records since the 1960s, with a style veering between soul, R&B, Celtic rock and jazz.

'Moondance' was written by Van Morrison and first appeared as the title track on the 1970 album *Moondance*. It has a strong jazz influence, using the Dorian mode and jazzy chords, and featuring swung rhythms and a punchy horn section.

'Moondance' was a hit again in 2003, when it was released by the Canadian singer Michael Bublé.

'Moondance' is marked 'Swung'. This means that you should think of all ♪ notes in pairs and put a little more emphasis on the first of each pair, making it slightly longer. To get the swing feel, practise singing the song while clicking your fingers on the off-beats.

Try speaking the text several times before you sing. This will help you relax into the style of the music and feel the swung rhythms naturally.

Remember that if this key doesn't suit your voice there is an alternative version available from www.trinityrock.com in a higher key.

'All the *night's* magic *seems* to *whisper* and *hush'*

PLAYBACK

For your exam, you can choose either Playback or Improvising (see page 42). If you choose Playback, you will be asked to perform some music you have not seen or heard before.

In the exam, you will be given the song chart and the examiner will play a recording of the music on CD. You will hear several two-bar or four-bar phrases on the CD: you should sing each of them straight back in turn. There's a rhythm track going throughout, which helps you keep in time. There should not be any gaps in the music.

In the exam you will have two chances to perform with the CD:
- First time – for practice
- Second time – for assessment.

You should listen to the audio, copying what you hear; you can also read the music from the song chart. Here are some practice song charts which are also on the CD in this book. The music is printed without text and may be sung to any vowel (with or without consonant) or to sol-fa. Some of the examples may include accents so you may need to use consonants or scat words for these to make them really obvious.

Practice playback 1

Practice playback 2

'*I* really *like* the *way* music *looks* on *paper*. It *looks* like *art* to *me*'

Steve Vai

SESSION SKILLS — IMPROVISING

For your exam, you can choose either Playback (see page 40), or Improvising. If you choose to improvise, you will be asked to improvise over a backing track that you haven't heard before in a specified style.

In the exam, you will be given a song chart and the examiner will play a recording of the backing track on CD. The backing track consists of a passage of music played on a loop. You should improvise a melody line over the backing track.

In the exam you will have two chances to perform with the CD:
- First time – for practice
- Second time – for assessment.

Here are some improvising charts for practice which are also on the CD in this book. The music is printed without text and may be sung to any vowel (with or without consonant) or to sol-fa.

Practice improvisation 1

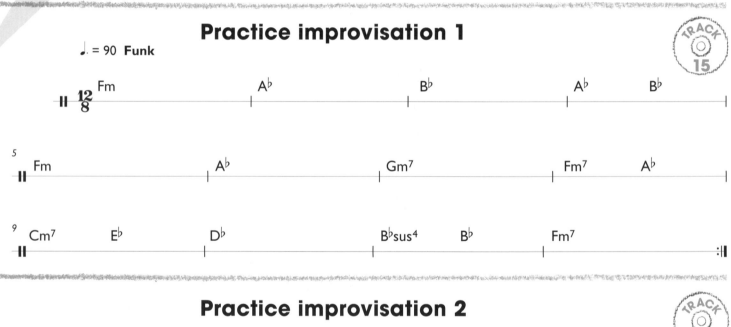

Practice improvisation 2

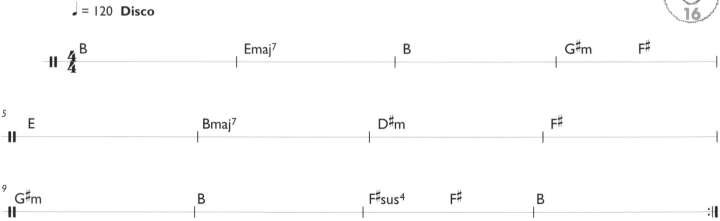

HELP PAGES

CHOOSING A SONG FOR YOUR EXAM

There are lots of options to help you choose your three songs for the exam.
For Songs 1 and 2, you can choose a song which is:

- from this book
- from www.trinityrock.com

Or for Song 2 you can choose a song which is:

- sheet music from a printed or online source
- your own arrangement of a song or a song you have written yourself (see page 44).

You can perform the song unaccompanied or with a backing track (minus the solo voice). If you like, you can create a backing track yourself (or with friends).

For Grade 5, the song should last between two and three-and-a-half minutes, and the level of difficulty should be similar to your other songs. When choosing a song, think about:

- Does it work for my voice?
- Are there any technical elements that are too difficult for me? (If so, perhaps save it for when you do the next grade.)
- Do I enjoy singing it?
- Does it work with my other songs to create a good set-list?

See www.trinityrock.com for further information and advice on choosing your own song.

SHEET MUSIC

You must always bring an original copy of the book or a download sheet with email certificate for each song you perform in the exam. If you choose to write your own song you must provide the examiner with a copy of the sheet music. Your music can be:

- a lead sheet with lyrics, chords and melody line
- a chord chart with lyrics
- a full score using conventional staff notation
- see page 44 for details on presenting a song you have written yourself.

The title of the song and your name should be on the sheet music.

WRITING YOUR OWN SONG

You can sing a song that you have written yourself for one of the choices in your exam. For Grade 5, your song should last between two and three-and-a-half minutes. It is sometimes difficult to know where to begin, however. Here are some suggestions for starting points:

- **A melody**: Many songs are made up around a hook (a short catchy melodic idea, usually only a few notes long). Try writing a couple of hooks:

- **Lyrics**: You could start by writing lyrics, or choosing someone else's lyrics (be aware of the copyright issues if you do this – see page 46 for further details). Your lyrics will help you decide whether your song will be upbeat or reflective, and may help you decide on a style and structure.

- **Structure**: Choose a structure for your song and write down a plan. For example, if you choose verse/chorus structure, your plan might be:

> verse: 12 bars, mainly E min and A min chords /
> chorus: 8 bars, G and D chords over two-bar bass riff /
> 2 x verses: 2 x 12 bars /
> final chorus: 8 bars + 4-bar coda (G and D chords)

You might consider including bridge sections, solo passages, or a pre-chorus.
Or you might like to use an entirely different structure: 12-bar blues, AABA (where the first idea is repeated, then followed by a different section before repeating again at the end) . . .

There are plenty of other ways of starting: perhaps with a riff or a chord sequence, for example. You will also need to consider what **instruments** it is for (solo voice or voice/keyboards/drums . . .).

There are many choices to be made – which is why writing a song is such a rewarding thing to do.

WRITING YOUR SONG DOWN

. . . .

Rock and pop music is often written as a **lead sheet** with the lyrics (if there are any), chords and a melody line.

- You may want to write your part on a **stave**, as has been used for the songs in this book.

- You can, if you prefer, use a **graph** or **table** to represent your music, as long as it is clear to anyone else (including the examiner) how the song goes.

HELP PAGES

PERFORMING IN A BAND

Performing in a band is exciting: it can be a lot of fun and, as with everything, the more you do it, the easier it gets. It is very different from performing on your own. Everyone contributes to the overall sound: the most important skill you need to develop is listening.

For a band to sound good, the players need to be 'together' – that mainly means keeping in time with each other, but also playing at the same volume, and with the same kind of feeling. Your relationship with the other band members is also important. Talk with them about the music you sing, the music you like, and what you'd like the band to achieve short-term and long-term.

Band rehearsals are important – you should not be late, tired or distracted by your mobile phone! Being positive makes a huge difference. Try to create a friendly atmosphere in rehearsals so that everybody feels comfortable trying out new things. Don't worry about making mistakes: that is what rehearsals are for.

'The Raggle Taggle Gypsies' on page 14 is arranged for band. You will find parts for guitar, bass keyboards and drums in the other Trinity Rock & Pop Grade 5 books. Trinity offers exams for groups of musicians at various levels. The songs arranged for bands are ideal to include as part of a song-list for these exams. Have a look at the website for more details.

HINTS AND TIPS

- Spend time planning your songs with the other band members. Think about who will play what, making the most of the instruments you have, and playing to the strengths of each band member. Be imaginative – the most exciting bands do not just copy what other bands have done, but play songs in new and unexpected ways.

- Record a demo. This can be a good way of giving the band a target to focus on. Make your demo the best you possibly can – record each song several times and discuss with the other band members which version works best. You can either record a demo in a studio, which enables you to edit your performances (combining the best bits of all your versions), or you can record your demo in 'live' conditions, which can give a more exciting demo but does not give you the opportunity to edit out any mistakes.

- Nothing beats the thrill of performing live in front of an audience. Organise a gig for a few friends. It can be a small gig in someone's house – the important thing is to get used to playing in front of other people. Gigs can be nerve-wracking at first, but try to relax and enjoy them.

HELP PAGES

SINGING WITH BACKING TRACKS

The CD contains demos and backing tracks of all the songs in the book. The additional songs at www.trinityrock.com also come with demos and backing tracks.

- In your exam, you should perform with the backing track, or you can create your own (see below).
- The backing tracks begin with a click track, which sets the tempo and helps you start accurately.
- Be careful to balance the volume of the backing track against your voice.
- Listen carefully to the backing track to ensure you are singing in time.

If you are creating your own backing track here are some further tips:

- Make sure the sound quality is of a good standard.
- Think carefully about the instruments/sounds you are putting on the backing track.
- Avoid copying what you are singing on the backing track – it should support not duplicate.
- Do you need to include a click track at the beginning?

COPYRIGHT IN A SONG

If you are a singer or songwriter it is important to know about copyright. When someone writes a song or creates an arrangement they own the copyright (sometimes called 'the rights') to that version. The copyright means that other people cannot copy it, sell it, perform it in a concert, make it available online or record it without the owner's permission or the appropriate licence. When you write a song you automatically own the copyright to it, which means that other people cannot copy your work. But, just as importantly, you cannot copy other people's work, or perform it in public without their permission or the appropriate licence.

Points to remember

- You can create a cover version of a song and play it in an exam or other non-public performance.
- You cannot record your cover version and make your recording available to others (by copying it or uploading it to a website) without the appropriate licence.
- You do own the copyright of your own original song, which means that no one is allowed to copy it.
- You cannot copy someone else's song without their permission or the appropriate licence.

ALSO AVAILABLE

Trinity College London Rock & Pop examinations 2012-2017 are also available for:

Bass Initial
ISBN: 978-0-85736-227-8

Bass Grade 1
ISBN: 978-0-85736-228-5

Bass Grade 2
ISBN: 978-0-85736-229-2

Bass Grade 3
ISBN: 978-0-85736-230-8

Bass Grade 4
ISBN: 978-0-85736-231-5

Bass Grade 5
ISBN: 978-0-85736-232-2

Bass Grade 6
ISBN: 978-0-85736-233-9

Bass Grade 7
ISBN: 978-0-85736-234-6

Bass Grade 8
ISBN: 978-0-85736-235-3

Drums Initial
ISBN: 978-0-85736-245-2

Drums Grade 1
ISBN: 978-0-85736-246-9

Drums Grade 2
ISBN: 978-0-85736-247-6

Drums Grade 3
ISBN: 978-0-85736-248-3

Drums Grade 4
ISBN: 978-0-85736-249-0

Drums Grade 5
ISBN: 978-0-85736-250-6

Drums Grade 6
ISBN: 978-0-85736-251-3

Drums Grade 7
ISBN: 978-0-85736-252-0

Drums Grade 8
ISBN: 978-0-85736-253-7

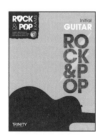

Guitar Initial
ISBN: 978-0-85736-218-6

Guitar Grade 1
ISBN: 978-0-85736-219-3

Guitar Grade 2
ISBN: 978-0-85736-220-9

Guitar Grade 3
ISBN: 978-0-85736-221-6

Guitar Grade 4
ISBN: 978-0-85736-222-3

Guitar Grade 5
ISBN: 978-0-85736-223-0

Guitar Grade 6
ISBN: 978-0-85736-224-7

Guitar Grade 7
ISBN: 978-0-85736-225-4

Guitar Grade 8
ISBN: 978-0-85736-226-1

Keyboards Initial
ISBN: 978-0-85736-236-0

Keyboards Grade 1
ISBN: 978-0-85736-237-7

Keyboards Grade 2
ISBN: 978-0-85736-238-4

Keyboards Grade 3
ISBN: 978-0-85736-239-1

Keyboards Grade 4
ISBN: 978-0-85736-240-7

Keyboards Grade 5
ISBN: 978-0-85736-241-4

Keyboards Grade 6
ISBN: 978-0-85736-242-1

Keyboards Grade 7
ISBN: 978-0-85736-243-8

Keyboards Grade 8
ISBN: 978-0-85736-244-5

Vocals Initial
ISBN: 978-0-85736-254-4

Vocals Grade 1
ISBN: 978-0-85736-255-1

Vocals Grade 2
ISBN: 978-0-85736-256-8

Vocals Grade 3
ISBN: 978-0-85736-257-5

Vocals Grade 4
ISBN: 978-0-85736-258-2

Vocals Grade 5
ISBN: 978-0-85736-259-9

Vocals Grade 6 (female voice)
ISBN: 978-0-85736-263-6

Vocals Grade 6 (male voice)
ISBN: 978-0-85736-260-5

Vocals Grade 7 (female voice)
ISBN: 978-0-85736-264-3

Vocals Grade 7 (male voice)
ISBN: 978-0-85736-261-2

Vocals Grade 8 (female voice)
ISBN: 978-0-85736-265-0

Vocals Grade 8 (male voice)
ISBN: 978-0-85736-262-9